Wild Edibles of Fresno County
Plus a Complete Section on Usable Herbs

Written by

Mike Rhodes

With all photographs by

Jim Ashbrook

and drawings by

David Cox

Acknowledgements

I would like to thank everyone I know for encouraging me along in this endeavor. Without your positive thoughts and suggestions, this book would have never become a reality. Specifically, I would like to thank Jim for taking the time to shoot some really great photographs and for all the time he has put into helping publish this book. Lenore Edwards, Chris Dunkle and Kim Werner also deserve special thanks for their help in editing, paste-up and typing.

Without the knowledge and guidance from people like Lang Russel and Stephanie Malone, who already knew which plants are edible and which are not, I probably could have never started this book. So I am especially indebted to their kindness and patience for showing me what plant is what.

I also would like to express my gratitude to Mr. Weiler, a botany professor at Fresno State University, for taking the time to identify many of the pictures that appear in this book.

For the third edition, Anne Haddix identified plants by their Latin names, which will aid more experienced botanists in their identification of edible plants. I have heard many botanists will consider this an invaluable asset to this book, and I'm particularly grateful to Anne for helping out.

For the fourth edition, I want to give a shout-out and many thanks to Michael D. Evans, who copyedited this book. When I first wrote *Wild Edibles* in 1974, I had no idea what a copyeditor did and now I can't imagine living without one. Thank you for improving the readability and accuracy and catching all of those pesky spelling errors.

Table of Contents

Edible Plants

Healing Herbs

Introduction to the Third Edition

In this, the third printing of *Wild Edibles*, I have corrected many of the problems of the previous editions and have added new, useful information. In the several years since this book was first published, many suggestions have been brought to my attention and have been incorporated in this edition to make it the most valuable ever. Pages are now numbered, there is a table of contents, plants are identified not only by their common names, but by their Latin names as well, and many better photos have been added since the first printing. Its purpose is to get the reader involved with nature in a personal way, and if the content keeps improving it is my belief that the goal will be better achieved. That is why this book is written in such a way that anyone, with a minimum of difficulty, can find in its pages almost any edible plant in the county and, after positively identifying it in the field, can put it to its proper use.

No plant should be wasted or used if it is not necessary. The Native Americans of our area were able to survive because they were relatively small in numbers and they knew how to live in harmony with their environment. They would never eat all of one variety of any plant in an area before the plant had gone to seed. Otherwise, there would be none next year. Our mountains cannot survive large numbers of city folks gathering their dinners in the wilds. My advice is to respect the natural balance of things by not devouring whole fields of any one variety.

This book is not written to encourage people to live directly off the land, as the Native Americans did, without other means of support. Local Native Americans were subjected to many hardships in order to live their free and natural lives. Besides spending much of their life in the search for food, the food they did eat consisted of what our culture might consider to be undesirable at best. Frogs, snakes, lizards and several kinds of insects were often eaten when other meat was scarce. It is truly questionable whether any of us in 20th century America could revert back to such a primitive lifestyle. Reading this book will, however, make it possible for you to survive for short durations in the wilds by eating what nature has to offer.

Information contained in this book also could be used to prepare delicious meals cooked entirely from wild foods. There are no doubt good tasting edible mushrooms here, however, it would be unwise for me to attempt to describe them. There are too many poisonous varieties that look like the edible kinds to make it worthwhile. I've heard of too many people being poisoned because they thought they knew what mushroom they were eating but obviously didn't. Mushrooms are too broad of a subject to be covered in this book or by people who don't have an abundance of time or enthusiasm for them. If you are interested, there are some good books on the subject at the downtown library.

In addition to edible plants, there is included a section on herbs. Before there was a modern medical profession, people relied largely on herbal remedies. Today, modern medicine is a highly technical skill known only by a few, but it still derives many of its healing agents from herbs and other plants. Locally found herbs listed in this book have long been used successfully for their medicinal properties, but in this age of specialization it is not legal for me to prescribe them as a doctor could. I must therefore state that the herbal remedies mentioned in this book are included only to pass information on as to how people healed themselves without the family doctor. This information is not meant to suggest that you discontinue seeing your doctor.

Introduction to the Fourth Edition

The book you have in your hands now is an updated version of the third edition, using the original photos and illustrations that were in storage for the last 45 years. The ability to "print on demand" has made this an entirely different experience from producing the book in 1974. At that time, a Selectric typewriter was the top-of-the-line technology for setting type, and I printed the book on a Multi 1250 press, folding, collating and stapling each book together. For the fourth edition, all I had to do was type it into a computer, scan the photos and send it to Amazon, which prints on demand and sends a copy to anyone who places an order.

Glossary

Acuminate: To taper to a needle like point, slender pointed, tapering

Acute: Sharp pointed, an angle of less than 90%

Alternate: Usually said of leaves when not opposite or whorled, but situated singly along the stem

Anodyne: Medicine that relieves pain

Antiscorbutic: Counteracting scurvy

Annual: A plant that lives only one year

Aromatic: A plant yielding or producing an aroma

Astringent: Having a harsh, biting quality

Basal: Situated at or near the base

Biennial: A plant that lives two years

Bract: a modified leaf, typically small, with a flower or flower cluster in its axil. bracts are sometimes larger and more brightly colored than the true flower, as in a poinsettia

Bramble: A tangle of prickly vines or bushes

Carminative: Medicine that is used for expelling gas from the body; relieving colic

Catarrh: Inflammation of a mucous membrane, increasing the output of mucous

Cathartic: Medicine good for cleansing your system

Cordate: Heart-shaped

Deciduous: A tree or plant with parts, such as flowers, fruits and leaves that fall after a definite period of growth

Demulcent: Soothing or softening application

Uentate: A leaf having a toothed edge

Dermatitis: Inflammation of the skin

Diaphoretic: An agent that tends to increase perspiration

Diuretic: A medicine that promotes secretion or discharge of urine

Elliptic: Having a shape two or three times long as wide

Emetic: An agent swallowed to induce vomiting

Evergreen: A tree or plant which retains its foliage all year

Expectorant: Promoting the secretion of fluid from the respiratory tract

Flail: An instrument for thrashing grain

Lance: Refers to leaves that are much longer than they are wide

Lobe: A part of any plant organ set off by indentations

Narcotic: A drug that alleviates pain and induces sleep

Oblong: A right-angled figure, unequal in length and breadth

Ointment: An oily preparation applied to wounds; a salve used to make the skin smooth and soft

Opposite: Leaves that meet at one point on a stem and appear to be opposite of each other

Ovate: Flat and egg-shaped with the broadest part near the base or below the middle

Palmately: Shaped like a hand with the fingers spread; having veins or lobes radiating from a common center

Panicle: A compound flower cluster in which the main stem branches into secondary stems, these bearing the flower stems and flowers, or even branching indefinitely

Perennial: A plant that lives from year to year

Petiole: The stalk of a leaf

Pinnate: A condition wherein the secondary veins of a leaf are arranged along the midrib, or when the leaflets of a compound leaf are arranged along a stalk and on each side of it

Poultice: A soft, moist, mass of herbs spread on a cloth and applied as a medicament to the body

Prostrate: Lying flat on the ground

Raceme: An open, unbranched, elongate flower cluster arranged along an axis

Sagittate: Shaped like an arrowhead

Scape: A long flower stem rising from a clump of leaves or from a covered part in the ground

Sepal: One of the outermost flower parts, usually green and usually just outside the petals

Sessile: This is where the leaf is without a stalk; it is attached directly by the base

Spike: A raceme-like flower cluster, but with the flowers sessile

Stimulant: Stimulants serve to quicken or increase various functional actions of the system

Stomachic: Acting as a digestive tonic

Sudorific: A medicine that causes sweating

Tonic: A strengthening medicine

Tuber: A fleshy, usually oblong outgrowth of a subterranean stem or shoot, such as the potato

Umbel: A flat-topped flower cluster with individual flower stalks arising from the same place

Vermifuge: A medicine to remove worms from the intestines

Flower & Leaf Types

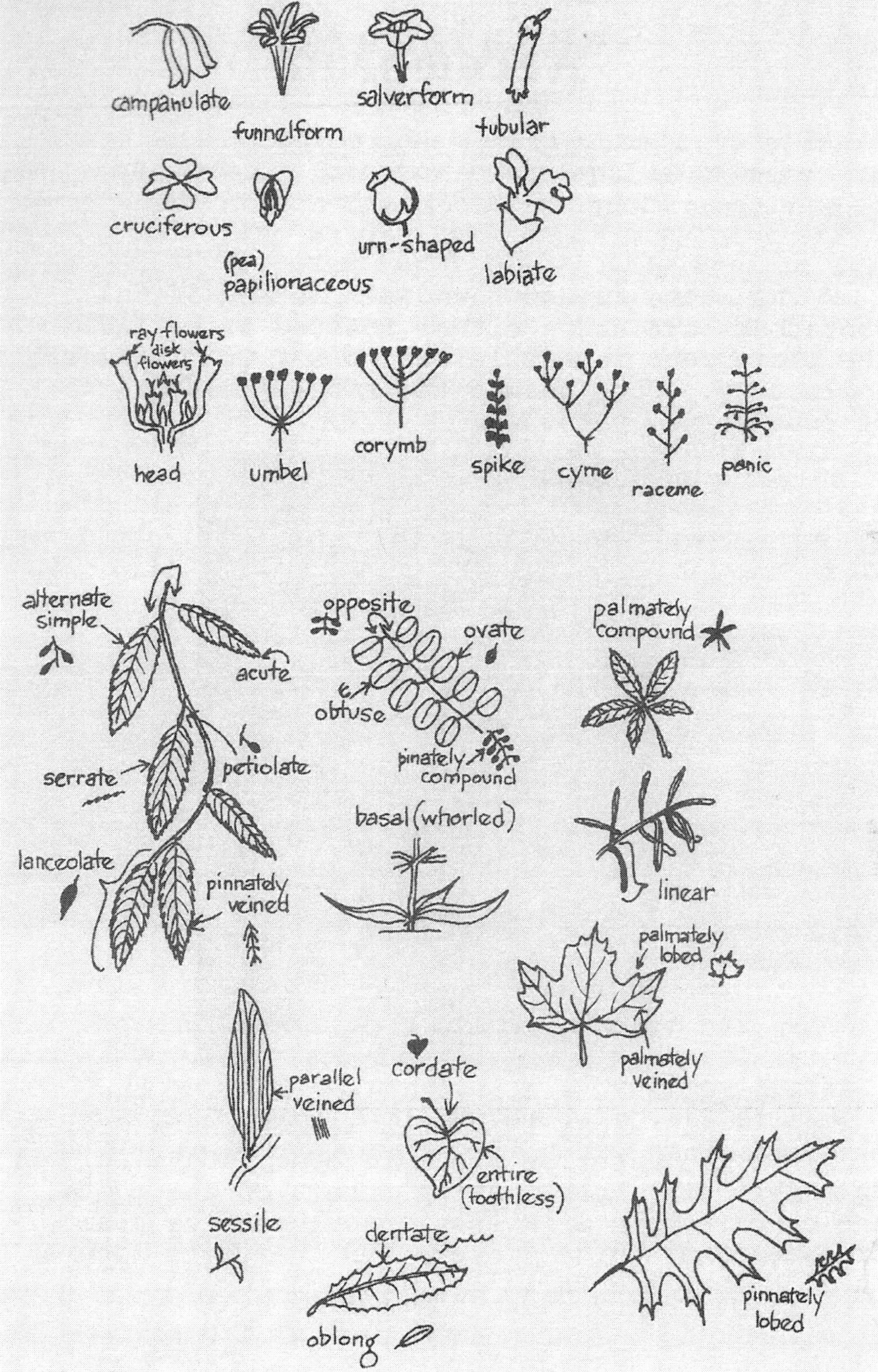

campanulate

funnelform

salverform

tubular

cruciferous

(pea) papilionaceous

urn-shaped

labiate

ray-flowers
disk flowers

head

umbel

corymb

spike

cyme

raceme

panic

alternate simple

acute

opposite

ovate

obtuse

palmately compound

serrate

petiolate

pinately compound

lanceolate

pinnately veined

basal (whorled)

linear

palmately lobed

palmately veined

parallel veined

cordate

entire (toothless)

sessile

dentate

oblong

pinnately lobed

11

Arrowhead
Sagittaria latifolia

Common names: Wappato, Duck Potato and Tule Potato

The white tubers found at the end of the rootstocks are eaten either roasted or boiled. The whole root is edible but is not usually worth collecting. When cooked, the tubers are said to be superior to potatoes.

Arrowhead is found in ponds and wet ground. The leaves look like arrowheads and either float on the water or are held erect above it. It is a perennial herb, having tubers on the roots, and containing a milky sap throughout the plant. Arrowhead has white flowers, and the roots mature in midsummer and fall.

Asparagus
Asparagus officinalis

The same variety that is sold in city stores grows free for the picking every spring in many parts of Fresno County. It's the young stalks that are of value before they begin branching off and turn into a large ferny bush. It's best to start off early in spring to find asparagus spears. An advantage in finding them is to locate last year's asparagus plant as the roots are perennial and thus will produce plants in the same area year after year. Last year's asparagus will be about three feet high with a central stem about one-half inch in diameter. The side branches are evenly spaced and tapered, giving the whole plant a slender Christmas tree outline. The ferny leaves are, of course, all dead and what remains is of a straw color.

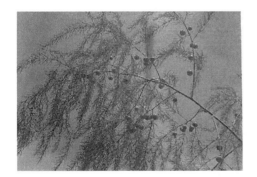  

Asparagus is still edible after it has grown ferny, but you probably wouldn't want to eat it unless it was out of necessity. The older stalks can be peeled and their insides eaten either raw or cooked in a thick soup. When the large ferny branches are cut back, before it is too late in summer, new tender shoots will be sent up for you to feast on.

Wild asparagus can be found growing on ditches and riverbanks, in fields and backyards or just about anywhere birds might carry their little red berries off to.

Blackberry

Rubus procerus

This bush grows on many ditches and riverbanks offering its delightful tasting berries to anyone with enough time and interest to pick them. When berries have turned from red to black, they are ready to be made into blackberry jam, wine or just eaten raw. A tea made of the roots or leaves makes a long used remedy for diarrhea.

This thorny plant, creating bramble, which grows best in almost full sun, has small white flowers that are replaced with red and then blackberries.

Brodiaea

Brodiaea elegans

Common name: Wild Hyacinth

This herb's bulb can be eaten raw, boiled for a few minutes or roasted for about half an hour. The young pods can be used as greens.

Brodiaea is a perennial herb with leaves that are basal, few and slender. The flowers appear in an umbel-like cluster, and the scape is 4–12 inches high. It can be found growing in the foothills and mountains.

Cattail
Typha latifolia

The cattail is a good find as it has many edible parts to offer. A flour, with an analysis similar to that of whole grains, can be made from the cattail root. Collect a quantity of the roots, peel the outside of the root off keeping the approximately half-inch core, then fill a large container with the roots and cold water. Crush the roots with your hands until the fibers are all separated and washed clean. Strain out the fibers, and allow the water to settle for half an hour. The flour will settle on the bottom. Pour out the water and add fresh water, stir up the flour and let settle again. Pour off the water and let the flour dry.

Before the cattail is mature, the inner part of the stem, close to the root, is edible. Pull up the whole plant, cut off the root and peel the outside stem back. The inner stem tastes much like cucumber.

Boil for a few minutes the young green spikes of cattail after removing the papery sheath that encloses them. Add butter, and you have a great tasting wild vegetable.

Pollen can be collected from that large cigar-shaped spike peculiar to cattails. Tap the pollen off into a bucket, and use it with or as flour.

Cattails grow in water along lakes and rivers, ditch banks and marshes. The mature plant is 4–7 feet high and is distinctive looking.

Cattail

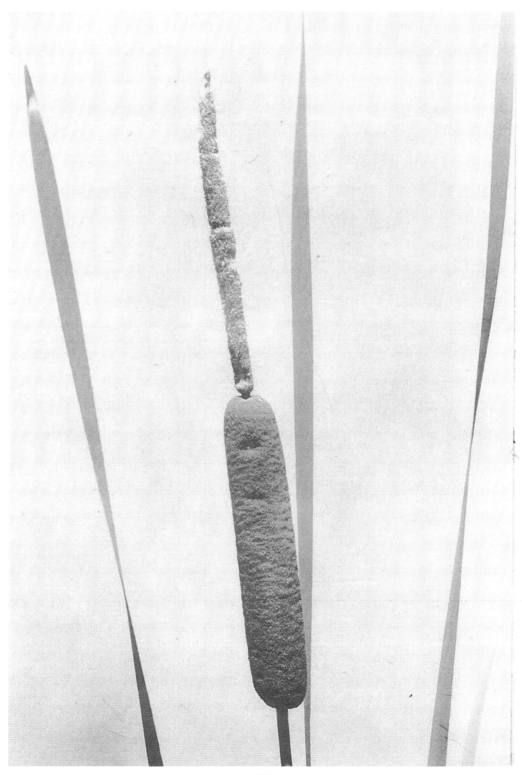

Chickweed

Stellaria media

The leaves are cooked like spinach. Seeds too are sometimes eaten raw. Large amounts of chickweed should not be eaten as they are reported to sometimes accumulate concentrations of nitrates at potentially toxic levels. Eaten in reasonable quantities, though, chickweed will not present a problem.

Chickweed grows from fall through winter and finishes its life cycle and seed production in spring. Chickweed will grow 6–15 inches in length, with a prostrate, brittle and leafy stem. The leaves are ovate-cordite with the lower ones on hairy petioles. The flowers are small and white.

Clover
Trifolium

A bread can be made from the seeds and dried blossoms of clover. In times of famine, this bread has been used as a mainstay and is considered extremely wholesome and nutritious.

Tea made from the dried flowers is given to those suffering from bronchitis, asthma and coughs and is recommended especially for whooping cough.

Clover is commonly found in lawns and the chances are good that it's growing in your lawn right now. Clover also can be found growing in pastures and fields.

Date Palm

The fruit that grows on the top of the tree is eaten either raw or dried.

There are many palm trees in this county, of which only a few are date palms. They are differentiated by their clusters of fruit at the top. Other palms have no fruit on the top. The stem is straight and tall, about the same thickness all the way up. Date palms grow 40–100 feet high, making it necessary to use a ladder to reach the fruit.

Elderberry

Sambucus Cerule

These berries can be used in several useful ways. They will make a fine tasting wine or a pretty good jam. A strong emetic can be extracted from the elder's inner bark. A hot poultice of elder leaves is said to relieve the pain and promote the healing of sprains and bruises.

Native Americans made flutes from the older stems as they have a rather soft pith that is easily removed with a small iron rod.

The elder is a bush or small tree getting 6–15 feet high with small white flowers in terminal clusters that turn into bluish berries. Its leaves are pinnate with 5–11 leaflets.

Gooseberry
Ribes viscossimum

Gooseberries can be eaten raw or cooked. They can also be dried for later use. Excellent pies and jellies are made with gooseberries.

The gooseberry is a shrub found fairly high in the mountains with palmately veined leaves. The sepals and petals number five and rarely four. The petals are shorter than the sepals. The fruit forms into a prickly berry.

Lamb's Quarters

Chenopodium album

The leaves are eaten (they're best before the plant reaches a foot high) like spinach. When collected, the seeds are used whole in breads or are sometimes crushed in flour.

The mature plants vary greatly in size. They range from one to six feet high with one main stem and are often branched. The flowers are small, inconspicuous, greenish and mealy in the bud. They are arranged in tight clusters at the tips of the stems or branches.

Lichens

Lichens are a bland and nutritious wild food. They should be soaked, dried and then soaked again for several hours. Cook the lichens for about 20 minutes and eat.

Lichens grow on rocks and trees and have parts of both fungus and algae making up their structure. They are green, grey, yellow, maroon, black or orange. Natural dyes are also made from lichens.

Loquat

Although grown only domestically here, the loquat should not be overlooked as a valuable food source for the hungry. Between April and July, hundreds of thousands of the loquat's tasty fruit ripens fall to the ground and rot becoming useful to no one. When the loquats are a yellow-orange color and some have begun to fall from the tree, it is then a good time to begin picking the tree. If the tree is obviously owned by someone who apparently does not care for the fruit, it would be a good idea to ask permission to have the unwanted fruit, saving the owner the burden of cleaning up what otherwise would have been wasted. Loquats are good raw or made into jams and jellies.

Manzanita

Arctostaphylos mariposa

The berries are usable mainly as a food source, and the leaves are used medicinally for their astringent properties, being useful for the relief of bronchitis. Native Americans used manzanita berries, eating them raw, ground into meal to be used as a porridge and as a drink. To derive a drink from the berries, they must first be crushed and then scalded with enough water to equal the bulk of the berries. When all of this settles and is strained, it makes a fine tasting drink.

Manzanita is an evergreen shrub with crooked branches and urn-shaped pink or white flowers in small nodding terminal clusters. Its berries are round and generally of a red or pink color. It is commonly found in the mountains above a few thousand feet.

Mariposa Lily
Calochortus amoenus

Common names: Star Tulip, Butterfly Tulip, Sego Lily and Cat's Ear

Eaten either raw or cooked the bulb tastes like potatoes. Because the bulbs are small, Native Americans collected many of them at once and steamed them in firepits or roasted them over a smoky fire. This, it is said, improves their flavor. When dried, the bulbs can be ground into flour.

The mariposa lily is found in open woods, valleys and elsewhere in dry to moist ground. Flowering stems rise from coated bulbs. The stems are simpler and sparingly branched. The leaves are few, alternate and narrow. The flowers range in color from pale yellow to nearly scarlet and from white to deep lavender.

Milkweed

Asclepias

There are many different ways in which milkweed can be used. They have young shoots up to six inches high that can be eaten like asparagus. Newly opened leaves can be served like spinach. The unopened flower pods are eaten like broccoli, and the young pods can be cooked like okra.

Milkweed is naturally bitter, and therefore it is necessary to leach this bitterness out. For cooking milkweed in any of the above ways, put it in a pot of boiling water and change the water several times with more boiling water. It is important that the fresh water be boiling, otherwise, the bitterness becomes fixed in the milkweed.

The milky substance that comes from breaking the stem is applied to ringworm, cuts, sores and warts. It will in most cases remove the wart or ringworm. The bark of the root also is used for medicinal purposes being a emetic, diaphoretic and expectorant.

Some varieties of milkweed can be toxic if eaten in large quantities, so it is suggested that you take it slow until you're sure the plant you are eating is OK. I've never heard of anyone poisoning themselves on this plant, but better to be safe than sorry.

Milkweed is most often found along roadsides, in waste places and about the edges of cultivated fields. It has rather stout stems and opposite-ovate leaves with wide central ribs. The plant's milky sap is often used as a guide to identify it by. But you should never identify milkweed by its milky secretion alone as there are many poisonous plants with milky sap.

Milkweed

Miner's Lettuce

Montia perfoliata

Miner's lettuce is used particularly in salads but can be eaten raw or in later spring cooked like spinach.

Miner's lettuce grows in the early spring in fields, pastures and along roadsides. It is easily identified by the way a pair of leaves grows together part of the way up some of the short stems and forms a cup through which the middle stalk continues.

Mustard

Brassica

The leaves are collected from the lower portion of the plant before it blooms. These make excellent greens that are high in vitamins A, B1, B2 and C, as well as many trace elements. For best results, cook for a full 30 minutes and pick before the weather has gotten too warm. If picked too late in the season, the mustard greens will be bitter.

Seeds also are usable in recipes, and when ground and mixed with flour and a little water they are useful to relieve sore muscles, aching backs and a congested chest. Make a paste of the above ingredients and spread thinly on a cloth and cover with another, and apply for 20 minutes to the affected area. To gather seeds collect plants just as the seed pods on the lower part of the plant are opening. Place the collected plants on a large sheet of plastic and let them dry for a few days. Then thrash out the seeds by beating them with a flail.

The many different varieties of mustard can be found growing just about everywhere under a few thousand feet elevation. It is considered a pest by farmers in the Valley. The leaves are lyre-shaped, 4–6 inches long on slender stems with large terminal lobes and several lateral lobes along the stem, all finely toothed around the edges. The leaves that appear on the flower stalk are smaller, almost stemless, and bitter. When in bloom, mustard is easily identified because of its bright yellow flowers.

Mustard

Nettle

Urtica urens

The leaves will lose their prickliness and become edible by dropping them into boiling water. These leaves are a good source of vitamins A and C.

Nettle juice can be substituted for rennet when making cheese. Rennet, which comes from the lining of the cow's stomach, is used to coagulate and harden the cheese.

Medicinally, nettle tea is a blood purifier and is used as a cure for rheumatism.

Nettle is familiar to anyone who has accidentally walked through the plant as its fine prickle contains formic acid, capable of causing a stinging irritation. When collecting nettle, always wear gloves or some sort of protection for your hands.

The leaves are opposite, cordate, lance-ovate and acuminate. The flowers are small and green. Nettle can be found along roadsides, in fields, in pastures and in the higher mountains.

Oak
Quercus

The oak's acorn provided a staple food for many Native American tribes of this area. They ground the hulled nuts in motors made in granite making a coarse meal that was then formed into cakes and baked in ovens. Because acorns are sometimes bitter, it might be necessary to leach out that bitterness. This is done by placing the shelled nuts into boiling water and replacing the water with fresh water every time it turns yellow. This should be done two or three times.

An antiseptic can be made from the infusion of leaves or powdered inner bark. Use these in a gargle against catarrh and colds. The acorn, when powdered also was used as an antiseptic and remedy for all kinds of poisons. This was added to wine or milk.

The oak is so common to this area that anyone who does not already know what it looks like will be familiar with it with no further description needed than the above picture.

Pigweed
Amaranthus retoflexus

Common names: Spreading Pigweed, Mat Amaranth, Prostrate Amaranth and Green Amaranth

The young leaves are used and cooked like greens. They should be used soon after gathering in order that their fine asparagus-like flavor can be kept. Pigweed is considered nutritionally superior to spinach.

Pigweed is a common annual that is found growing along roadsides, on farmlands and in backyards. It forms a mat from one-half to two feet across. Its stems are widely branched and light green; the leaves are green and one-quarter to three-quarters of an inch long. It has green inconspicuous flowers that are borne on short spikes at the base of the short leafstalks or branches.

Pine

Pinus sabiniana

The pine tree with its many different edible parts literally has saved hundreds of people from starvation. If you're hungry and do not wish to stop for a meal, pine needles are nutritious, pleasant tasting when new and starchy, and will ward off hunger. When there is more time, the tree's inner bark can be eaten either raw or cooked. If eaten cooked, it is best to cut it into thin strips and cook it like spaghetti. Dried, the inner bark can be ground into flour and mixed with regular flour. Of course, the pine nuts are the most familiar edible part of the pine and can be used in many ways, such as in salads, cookies, made into a flour, a nut loaf and many more good tasting meals.

The pine in the above photo is of a digger pine. There are, however, about a dozen other varieties of pines in our foothills and mountains. A good book to look at that goes in depth about these and other trees is *Discovering Sierra Trees* by Stephen F. Arno.

Prickly Lettuce

Lactuca scerariola

The young prickly lettuce is good to eat raw but later becomes too thorny and must be boiled to lose the prickliness.

In addition to being edible, the prickly lettuce will serve as a compass; its sharply toothed leaves twist edgewise to the sun and point north and south.

Prickly lettuce is an annual, 2–5 feet high with leaves that are sessile or sagittate, clasping 2–7 inches long, soft-prickly beneath. It is common and grows in fields, along roadsides and in waste places throughout the Valley and into the mountains.

Purslane

Portulaca oleracea

Common name: Mexican Spinach

The tender leaves of purslane are good both raw and cooked, from June until frost. It has a mucilaginous quality, like that of okra, which adds to the consistency of soups and stews.

Often considered a pesky weed, purslane grows low, not getting more than two inches off the ground, but spreading often times more than a foot across. The stem from where it starts can be one-quarter-inch think. Tiny yellow flowers bloom only on sunny mornings. They're found in the workings of the stems. Purslane has succulent reddish-purple stems and small fat leaves.

Rose
Rosa

The rose, which is grown in almost every yard in the county's towns for its beauty, also grows wild throughout the county's mountainous regions. This commonly known shrub has fragrant flowers, which after they fall form a ball called a reshape. This reshape is cut in half, dried and then a pleasant tasting tea can be brewed that is high in vitamin C.

A jam made by boiling down the hips gives a product of a rich orange color and interesting flavor.

Shepherd's Purse

Capsella bursa-pastoris

The leaves when young and tender are edible both cooked or raw. After being roasted, the seeds too can be eaten.

Shepherd's purse has been attributed to having many medicinal uses. When made into a tea, it is said to be somewhat cathartic and a definite diuretic. It also makes a fine remedy for bruises and to stop bleeding. Shepherd's purse has been used at times as a stimulant and anti scorbutic.

This common roadside plant is made familiar by the flattened pods at the end of its branching stems, which are said to resemble a shepherd's purse.

Soap Root

Chlorogalum pomeridianun

As the name suggests, the root of this plant is used as a soap. After removing the brown fibers from around the root, the center is crushed and rubbed vigorously to produce a lather. The brown fibers when dried are used as a fine-toothed comb. The root also can be eaten and is best after being thoroughly boiled.

Soap Root stands 1–3 feet high with narrow fluted leaves. It has a large brown fibrously coated bulb and large white flowers with green veins.

Sunflower

Helianthus annuus

This native plant provides dark gray seeds that are excellent to eat raw. Sunflower oil can be extracted by boiling the crushed seeds and then skimming the oil from the surface of the water.

The tubers of all sunflowers are edible, although some will be somewhat fibrous. Tubers from the Jerusalem artichoke are especially large and nutritious. They can be eaten raw, roasted or boiled.

They are perennial but most commonly annual herbs with simple leaves that are either opposite or alternate. The flower heads are large and solitary or a few in a bunch. The ray flowers are yellow, and the inside disk is yellow, purple or brown.

Thistle

Silybum maianum

The root is the only edible part of thistle. It can be peeled and eaten raw, boiled or roasted.

Thistle is a common biennial or perennial herb with spiny bracts surrounding the flowers. The spiny leaves are alternate, toothed or lobed. The flowerhead is rather large being of a purple, pink, red or sometimes yellowish or white color.

Watercress

Nasturtium officinale

Watercress when found will be one of your most desirable finds while hunting for food and nourishment. It is literally packed with vitamins, minerals and trace elements. The high vitamin C content of watercress makes it good for clearing up colds and sinus complaints. When juiced, it is said to be useful as a lotion for skin blemishes.

When picking, break off only the stems, leaving the roots undisturbed as the roots are inedible anyway and will produce more watercress if not destroyed. Eat the leaves and stems in salads, sandwiches or as cooked greens. A tea can also be made from the dried leaves. In areas where sheep or cattle abound, you should be particularly careful of eating watercress without thoroughly cleaning it. Liver flukes can be a danger in these areas.

Watercress can be found growing year-round in many shallow and slow-moving streams and creeks in the mountains. It has branching stems 1–2 feet long. The leaves are fleshy, elliptical and in pairs of three to seven. The flowers are small and white.

Wild Oat

Avena fatua

The seed is edible, but the hairs must be singed off before grinding into flour.

This annual grass abundantly grows in orchards and vineyards and along roadsides, ditch banks and fencerows. The mature plant is 1–4 feet tall with several stems arising from the base. The leaf blades are 3–10 inches long, one-quarter to one-half inch wide, thin and rough.

Wild Onion

Allium

Today, onions are used chiefly for flavoring but to the Native Americans they were a staple and eaten in great quantities. Wild onions can be used the same way domestic onions are used such as in soups, salads and stews.

All wild onions are edible and have that same unmistakable oniony smell. They grow from basal bulbs; their leaves can be tubular or flat, and the flowers are borne in a terminal umbel on a naked scape.

When identifying wild onions, be sure to use your sense of smell as some bulbs that appear superficially like that of onions are among the most concentrated poisons. All members of the onion genus, however, are nonpoisonous and have the same characteristic odor.

Healing Herbs

The plants in this section are reputed to have definite healing powers. The ones I have tried have all worked, and friends who have used the rest claim that they also work as described. Doctors extract remedies from some of these plants to use in their expensive little pills, and sick animals make use of these free and natural healers.

To get the most out of these herbals, you might want to try this exercise. Close your eyes and try to imagine the herb being used in its most natural, must vital, most living form. Picture it growing in a field, bathed in bright sunshine, alive and healthy, producing within its stems, leaves and flowers potent substances to heal you. Concentrate on this source. Know in your mind that this life force itself is absolutely positive and pure. As you are taking the herb, say to yourself, "I am taking the source, and its positive energy and healing power will heal me."

Herbs should be gathered in the morning and from plants that have not been damaged by insects. The healthier the plant the more useful the medicinal values will be. After picking, it is a good idea to wash the herbs to remove dirt, dead insects, spiders and the like.

Dry your herbs out of direct sunlight at room temperature in as dry and dark of an environment as is convenient. Herbs can be put in bags to dry (one variety of herb to a bag), hung on walls with string or any number of other ways. If all the above conditions are right and the drying herbs are well ventilated, it might take only a week for them to dry. But if it's cold or humid, it might take months so you might want to put them into a low oven (about 100 degrees) to speed up things.

Ailments and Cures

(Read the individual information about each herb before using it)

Aging, prevents: Chamomile
Bleeding: Shepherd's Purse
Bronchial irritations: Yerba Santa and Clover
Bruises: Shepherd's Purse
Colds: Watercress, Yarrow, Rose Hips and Mountain Misery
Coughs: Mullein, Clover and Mallow
Cuts and sores: Curly Dock and Goldenrod
Diarrhea: Blackberry
Digestion aid: Goldenrod
Hay fever: Yerba Santa
Headaches and migraine headaches: Rosemary
Hemorrhoids: Mullein
Kidney and bladder complaints: Mallow, Mugwort and Goldenrod
Nausea: Spearmint
Nerves: Mistletoe and Chamomile
Oral disorders (sores and eruptions on the tongue and gums): Pennyroyal
Pain reliever: Mullein
Rheumatism: Mountain Misery
Ringworm: Milkweed
Skin blemishes: Watercress
Sore muscles: Mustard
Stimulative: Goldenrod, Shepherd's Purse and Peppermint
Stomach upset: Peppermint
Swollen glands: Mullein
Vitamin deficiency: Dandelion
Vomiting: Spearmint
Wart removal: Milkweed and Mullein
Worms: Lupin

Chamomile

Anthemis cotula

Common name: Mayweed

A good tasting tea that is a depressant can be made from chamomile. It is said by ancient herbalists to prevent aging and is known by modern scientists to contain calcium, chlorine, potassium and silicon.

There is a weed that grows all over the county called pineapple weed, which is frequently mistaken for chamomile. It is much smaller and has no white petals on the flowers. The only similarity is the scent.

The real chamomile is about a foot high, with alternate leaves, finely dissected into linear lobes. The strong scented herb has daisy-like flowers. The inner disk of the flower is yellow, and the outside rays are white. The flowers appear in early summer after most spring wildflowers have quit blooming. The blooms last all summer and into fall.

Curly Dock

Rumex crispus

The leaves make for good greens but variation within the species can be somewhat sour or bitter. Therefore, it is suggested that they be mixed with greens from another wild vegetable. The roots, when washed, split in two parts and dried, are valuable in curing infections of the skin. The leaves also can be washed and laid on sores as a healing agent.

Dock is a perennial herb, with lance-shaped curly-edged leaves. The root is long and literally defies any attempt to pull it up. It grows almost everywhere, such as on ditch banks and in backyards, trash heaps and vacant lots.

Dandelion
Taraxacum officinale

This is one of those valuable herbs that most people consider a pest. Dandelion has a long history of use by ancient herbalists. They would dig the root and extract the juice giving it to those who were deficient in vitamins. The herbalists would then advise them to eat all the dandelion leaves they could find when spring came.

To eat dandelion leaves, it is important to pick them well before the plant blooms and as early in spring as possible. Otherwise, they can be so bitter that they're inedible. To cook the young leaves, boil in water only two or three minutes and serve with butter.

A natural coffee can be brewed from dandelion roots. Simply collect the roots, clean them, dry them in an oven (about 200 degrees) until they are crisp enough to snap, crush and add to boiling water. There are directions for making dandelion wine on the Internet.

The leaves are shining green in color, sessile and pinnate. Dandelion has yellow flowers that turn into small fluffy balls containing the seeds. Children have fun with these, blowing all the seeds off to tell their fortune. The root of the dandelion, when broken, exudes a milky substance.

Fennel

Foeniculum vulgare

Fennel is commonly used for its aromatic properties and is therefore blended with other teas to produce a pleasant taste or scent. The tea makes an excellent eye wash and has carminative and stomachic properties. The tea also is used to expel poisons from the body.

It is a perennial herb, 4–6 feet high, with striate branching stems. The leaves are numerous and slender with three shaped divisions. When crushed, the leaves have a licorice smell to them.

Goldenrod

Solidago californica

Common names: Aron's Rod and Blue Mountain Tea

A fine tasting tea can be made with goldenrod, which is stimulating and is a carminative when cold. It keeps health and relieves digestion in children. Goldenrod has long been used to help kidney stones and relieve ulcer pains. Soldiers from centuries past knew the value of goldenrod for healing external wounds. When wounded, they would apply leaves directly to the wound as soon as possible.

This perennial herb has a slender erect stem, sessile leaves covered with transparent dots and deep yellow flowers. The leaves have a fragrant odor, somewhat like that of anise and a warm aromatic agreeable taste. Flowers are arranged in terminal panicled racemes.

Horehound

Marrubium vulgare

The dried plant becomes a good nutritious tonic when made into a bitter tea or broth. In large doses, it becomes a laxative. Today, the use of horehound is limited almost entirely to the production of horehound candy and often is used to ease sore throats or cough. Horehound was once used extensively in domestic medicines for colds, dyspepsia and expelling worms.

Horehound is found in dry, open ground, especially waste places, throughout the West. The erect clustered stems branch from the base and are densely covered, to the point of being woolly, with white or greenish hairs. The leaves are roundish to oval, and the flowers are white to purplish.

Lupine
Lupinus formosus

Two or three lupine seeds can be used when a vermifuge is needed. They also are helpful in normalizing a woman's menstruation. Used externally, the powdered seeds help to clear up several forms of dermatitis.

Native Americans used the seeds in a tea as a diuretic. They also collected the leaves and flowers in early spring, stemmed them and ate them with acorn soup.

Lupine has palmately compound leaves, pea like flowers and seed pods on long stalks. The flowers are blue, yellow, white, purple or reddish in color. There are as many different varieties of lupine in California as there are of mammals.

Mallow
Malva parviflora

Common names: Malva and Cheeseplant

The name *mallow* is derived from the Greek word *malassein,* which means "to soften." Besides being a demulcent, mallow is a natural emollient, the tea being good for coughs due to colds and irritations of the air passages. It is used as a cleansing herb and for relief from various kidney and bladder complaints.

After the flowers have died, button-like seeds appear that are edible and have a nutty taste.

Mallow grows in fields and alleys, along roadsides and in the mountains. The plant is rather easy to identify because of its large deep green downy leaves, which are alternate on the stem. The flowers are numerous, purple and trumpet shaped. Early spring is the time you can find this plant in Fresno County.

Mint

There are many varieties of mint in our county almost all of which will make a good tasting tea. The leaves can be chewed as a breath freshener or be used for making jelly.

Medicinally, peppermint is a stimulative and is recognized as one of the most reliable household remedies for stomach ailments. Spearmint tea, which is a diuretic, has many uses; it is recommended against nausea and vomiting and can be used to combat high fevers.

Mentha spicata   *Mentha piperita*

Mint is found in wet places mostly in the mountains but sometimes along canals or low spots in the valley. There is a strong aromatic odor peculiar to mint. The stems are always square and the leaves sharply toothed. The flowers can be white, pink or violet in color.

Mistletoe

Phoradendron flavescens

When a tea is made from one teaspoonful of mistletoe to a pint of boiling water, it is a tonic and narcotic tea useful for calming nerves. Avoid the white berries as they are poisonous and can cause death.

Mistletoe is familiar to most everyone as the plant is hung over doorways and on ceilings around Christmas time. Growing as a parasite on the branches of deciduous trees, its roots penetrate into the host tree's bark and into the wood. Mistletoe is an evergreen.

Mountain Misery

Chamaebatia foliolosa

Common name: Bear Clover

Mountain misery gets its name because of the sticky resin that gets on your clothes. Despite its name, it does several beneficial uses. The Native Americans used it frequently in a decoction for coughs and colds. It is useful for the pains of rheumatism and for skin eruptions. It is sometimes used as a medicine to treat venereal diseases.

This mountain shrub grows up to two feet high with small, white strawberry-like flowers. The leaves are finely directed and fern-like.

Mugwort
Artemisia douglasiana

Common names: California Mugwort and Wormwood

A tea made with mugwort is good for those suffering from kidney stones and menstrual cramps. The leaves, when crushed or juiced, make an antiseptic wash.

Herbalists from ages past used mugwort to restore health to those who had taken drugs of a narcotic or euphoric nature.

This perennial herb which is found frequently on ditch banks and in pastures, grows 3–7 feet high with slender to stout stems that arise from running rootstocks. The leaves are 2–6 inches long, and the lower ones have 3–5 deep notches or lobes. The upper leaves have fewer sharply pointed lobes or are smooth around the margins. There are silvery and green varieties that grow here.

Mullein

Verbascum thapsus

Common names: Aaron's Rod, Adam's Flannel, Bullock's Lungwort and Velvet Dock

Mullein has been noted to be a demulcent, diuretic, anodyne and antispasmodic. A tea can be made for the relief of coughs and cramps.

To relieve the itching of piles, swollen glands, hemorrhoids and warts make a fomentation of the leaves in hot vinegar and water and apply externally. Mullein also makes a bright yellow dye. Many people smoke the dried leaves for the relief of coughs.

Mullein is identified by its straight, tall, stout, wooly, simple stem. The leaves are alternate, oblong, acute and feel like velvet on both sides. The flowers are yellow, and the plant grows 4–5 feet high. It grows on riverbanks, in recent clearings and along roadsides.

Pennyroyal
Mentha pulegium

Many insects avoid pennyroyal's aromatic odor. That is why it is often used in flea collars for cats and dogs. It also can be rubbed on the skin as an insect repellent.

The leaves can be chewed as a remedy for various oral disorders such as sores and eruptions on the tongue and gums. A tea made from pennyroyal is good for catarrh, chills, colds and coughs.

The stem is square (mint family), woody, branching from below and a foot or two high. The leaves are an inch or less long, toothed or entire with conspicuous veins. The flowers are purple in a dense head subtended by a number of ovate, green bracts.

Plantain

Plantago lanceolata

Plantain can be eaten either raw or cooked, but its real virtue is as a medicinal herb. Ancient Roman herbalists claimed that it would heal snakebites (including rattlesnake), but today it is used somewhat more modestly to cure cuts and sores. The plant has astringent properties and is good for diarrhea, colitis and hemorrhoids.

Found everywhere, even as a lawn pest, plantain's leaves all radiate from the base; they are lanceolate, sharply pointed and on long trough stems. The leaves are dark green in color and are strongly ribbed lengthwise. The flower stem is stiff and smooth and attains heights of 6–18 inches.

Rosemary

When looking for rosemary, the one thing that really gives it away is the smell, which is familiar to most people who do a little cooking. Other than that, the leaves are sessile, opposite and linear, over an inch in length and downy. Rosemary is an evergreen.

Yarrow
Achillea millefolium

Common names: Milfoil, Thousand-Seal, Wild Pepper, Angel Flower and Goose Tongue

Yarrow belongs to the aromatic class of sudorific tonics. When used for breaking a fever, cayenne pepper should be added to the tea. This will create a heavy sweat. Yarrow tea also is used for the relief of colds and for hair and scalp care.

It is good to drink anytime even if you have no other reason than wishing to enjoy a nice tasting herbal drink. The leaves are best picked in the early spring, thus avoiding the bitterness that you will surely find if you wait until later in summer.

Yarrow is to be found growing 1–3 feet high along roads and in pastures and meadows. It has a simple stem branched at the top and many crowded, alternate and dentate leaves spread upon the ground, finely cut and divided into many parts. The flowers are white, yellow or rose colored and in knots that come from the green stalks rising from among the leaves.

Yerba Santa

Eriodictyon californicum

Common names: Mountain Balm, Bears Weed and Holy Herb

Yerba santa is considered a good expectorant and hay fever remedy. It also is used to stop spasms of asthma and throat and bronchial irritations. A good herbal smoke that has medicinal values can be made by combining the dried leaves of yerba santa with a mint such as spearmint or peppermint.

Yerba santa grows 2–4 feet high and is an evergreen shrub found on dry mountain hills. The stem is smooth but exudes a gummy substance. The leaves are glutinous, 3–4 inches in length alternately on the stem, oblong or oval, lance-shaped, narrowing gradually to depressed veins. The underside contains many veins and has a varnished appearance. The flowers are whitish or pale blue in clusters at the top of the plant. The seed capsule is oval, grayish brown and contains small reddish-brown shriveled seeds.

Suggested Reading

The Herbalist
Joseph Meyer

Edible Plants
Bradford Angier

Herb Growing for Health
Donald Law

Stalking the Good life
Euell Gibbons

Stalking the Wild Asparagus
Euell Gibbons

The Complete Herbal
Ben Charles Harris

Culpeper's Complete Herbal
Nicholas Culpeper

Back to Eden
Jethro Kloss

Wild Edible Plants of the Western United States
Donald R. Kirk

A Modern Herbal - Two Volumes
Mrs. M. Grieve

Common Edible and Useful Plants of the West
Muriel Sweet

If you look hard enough, there's no telling what you might find.

Made in United States
Orlando, FL
17 January 2022

13617476R00039